The First-Time Mom's Guid
Need to Know for a F

Lucas Novak

TABLE OF CONTENTS

Chapter 1: The Journey Begins: Preparing for Motherhood

Choosing to Become a Mom

Becoming a mother is a life-changing decision that is both exciting and overwhelming. For many women, the desire to become a mom is innate and can be a dream they have had since childhood. However, for others, the decision to start a family may require careful consideration and planning. In this subchapter, we will explore the various factors involved in choosing to become a mom, helping new moms navigate this important decision.

One of the first steps in deciding to become a mom is self-reflection. Ask yourself why you want to have a baby and what it means to you. Is it because you feel ready to nurture another life, or are you succumbing to external pressures? Understanding your motivations will help you make an informed decision.

Next, consider your current circumstances. Assess your emotional and financial readiness for parenthood. Are you in a stable relationship or prepared to embark on the journey as a single parent? Finances play a crucial role in raising a child, so analyze your budget and make sure you can provide for your baby's needs.

It's also important to evaluate your support system. Having a strong network of family and friends can be invaluable during the early stages of motherhood. Reach out to loved ones and discuss your plans with them. Their input and guidance can offer valuable insights and help you make an informed decision.

Educate yourself about the realities of motherhood. Read books, speak to experienced moms, and attend parenting classes. Understanding the challenges and responsibilities that come with being a mom will help you make an informed decision. Additionally, consider your career aspirations and how motherhood might impact your professional goals. Many women successfully balance motherhood and career, but it's important to assess your priorities and decide what is best for you.

Finally, trust your instincts. Only you can truly know if you are ready to become a mom. Listen to your gut feelings and take your time in making this life-changing decision. Remember, there is no one-size-fits-all approach to motherhood, and every woman's journey is unique.

Choosing to become a mom is a personal and transformative decision. By taking the time to reflect, evaluate your circumstances, and educate yourself, you will be better equipped to navigate the joys and challenges of motherhood. Trust your instincts and embrace this incredible journey with an open heart.

Preconception Planning

Planning for pregnancy is an essential step on the journey to motherhood. Preconception planning involves taking proactive measures to ensure a healthy pregnancy, both for you and your baby. This subchapter will guide you through the key aspects of preconception planning, providing you with the knowledge and tools to make informed decisions.

Before you start trying to conceive, it is crucial to schedule a preconception appointment with your healthcare provider. During this visit, your doctor will assess your overall health, review your medical history, and discuss any potential risk factors. They will also provide guidance on lifestyle changes, such as adopting a healthy diet, maintaining a regular exercise routine, and avoiding harmful substances like tobacco, alcohol, and drugs.

In addition to lifestyle adjustments, preconception planning involves understanding your menstrual cycle and identifying your most fertile days. Learning how to track your ovulation can greatly increase your chances of conceiving. This subchapter will explore various methods of ovulation tracking and help you determine which one suits you best.

Furthermore, preconception planning also includes genetic counseling for certain individuals or couples with a family history of genetic disorders. This process involves assessing the likelihood of passing on genetic conditions to your child and discussing available options for managing or preventing these conditions.

Financial planning is another crucial aspect to consider before embarking on your motherhood journey. This subchapter will provide guidance on budgeting, insurance coverage, and utilizing resources available to new moms, such as government assistance programs or employer benefits.

Lastly, preconception planning addresses emotional readiness. Becoming a mother can bring about a range of emotions, from excitement to anxiety. It is important to have open and honest conversations with your partner, family, and friends about your expectations, concerns, and support systems. This subchapter will offer tips on building a strong support network and preparing mentally and emotionally for the changes that lie ahead.

Remember, preconception planning is not meant to overwhelm but to empower you. By taking the necessary steps outlined in this subchapter, you are setting the foundation for a healthy and happy pregnancy, preparing yourself physically, mentally, and emotionally to welcome your little bundle of joy into the world.

Understanding Pregnancy

Pregnancy is a beautiful and transformative journey that marks the beginning of motherhood. For new moms, this experience can be both exciting and overwhelming. In this subchapter, we will delve into the various aspects of pregnancy, providing you with a comprehensive understanding of this miraculous time in your life.

First and foremost, it is essential to understand the basics of pregnancy. Pregnancy typically lasts for about 40 weeks, divided into three trimesters. During this time, your body undergoes significant changes to accommodate the growth and development of your baby. From conception to birth, your body becomes a nurturing space for new life.

One of the first signs of pregnancy is a missed period, which signals the possibility of conception. Other early signs may include fatigue, nausea, breast tenderness, and frequent urination. Once you suspect you might be pregnant, it is crucial to confirm with a home pregnancy test or a visit to your healthcare provider.

As your pregnancy progresses, you may experience a wide range of physical and emotional changes. From morning sickness to mood swings, these symptoms are normal and vary from woman to woman. It is important to listen to your body and seek medical advice if you have any concerns.

Throughout your pregnancy, prenatal care is vital for the well-being of both you and your baby. Regular check-ups with your healthcare provider will help monitor your baby's growth, ensure proper nutrition, and detect any potential complications. Additionally, maintaining a healthy lifestyle, including a balanced diet and regular exercise, can greatly contribute to a smooth and healthy pregnancy.

Understanding the different stages of fetal development is also crucial for new moms. From the moment of conception, your baby begins to grow and develop rapidly. We will explore the major milestones your baby reaches during each trimester, helping you visualize their progress and fostering a deeper connection with your little one.

Lastly, we will touch upon common discomforts during pregnancy and offer practical tips to alleviate them. From morning sickness to backaches and swollen feet, we will provide natural remedies and lifestyle adjustments to help you navigate these challenges.

Remember, every pregnancy is unique, and this guide aims to provide a general understanding of what to expect. Your healthcare provider will be your best resource for personalized information and guidance throughout this incredible journey.

Embrace the joy and anticipation of pregnancy, and let this guide be your companion as you embark on the path to becoming a first-time mom.

Nurturing Your Body and Mind during Pregnancy

Pregnancy is a beautiful and transformative journey, filled with joy, anticipation, and sometimes, a few challenges. As a first-time mom, it's essential to prioritize your physical and mental well-being during this incredible time. Nurturing your body and mind not only ensures a healthier pregnancy but also sets the foundation for a happy and fulfilling life with your baby. In this subchapter, we will delve into valuable tips and advice to help you navigate this transformative period with confidence and grace.

Taking care of your body is crucial during pregnancy. Ensure you are getting the right nutrients by maintaining a well-balanced diet. Incorporate plenty of fruits, vegetables, whole grains, lean proteins, and healthy fats into your meals. Stay hydrated and consider adding prenatal vitamins to supplement your nutritional needs.

Regular exercise is equally important for a healthy pregnancy. Engage in low-impact activities like walking, swimming, or prenatal yoga to stay active and maintain your fitness levels. Consult your healthcare provider for exercise recommendations tailored to your individual needs.

Pregnancy can also take a toll on your mental health, which is why nurturing your mind is essential. Take time for self-care activities that bring you joy and relaxation. Whether it's reading a book, taking a warm bath, meditating, or practicing deep breathing exercises, find what helps you unwind and rejuvenate.

Educating yourself about pregnancy and childbirth can alleviate any anxiety or concerns you may have. Read books, attend prenatal classes, and seek advice from experienced moms or healthcare professionals.

Knowledge empowers you to make informed decisions and enables you to navigate this journey confidently.

Surround yourself with a supportive network of loved ones and other new moms. Join online or in-person support groups where you can share your experiences, seek advice, and find solace in knowing that you are not alone in this journey.

Lastly, prioritize regular prenatal check-ups with your healthcare provider to monitor your baby's growth and address any concerns promptly. These appointments are also an opportunity to discuss any physical or emotional changes you may be experiencing.

Remember, nurturing your body and mind during pregnancy is not a luxury but a necessity. By taking care of yourself, you are creating a solid foundation for your baby's well-being. Embrace this incredible journey, trust your instincts, and enjoy every precious moment as you prepare to welcome your little one into the world.

Chapter 2: Embracing Pregnancy: A Time of Change and Growth

Physical Changes and Symptoms

As a new mom, you are embarking on an incredible journey filled with joy, excitement, and a few physical changes. Pregnancy brings about many transformations in your body, some of which may surprise you. Understanding these changes and being prepared for the associated symptoms can help you navigate this incredible experience with ease and confidence.

One of the most noticeable physical changes during pregnancy is the growth of your belly. As your baby develops and grows, your abdomen expands to accommodate their needs. Embrace this change and proudly flaunt your baby bump, as it is a beautiful symbol of the new life growing within you.

Weight gain is another common physical change that occurs during pregnancy. While it is essential for the healthy development of your baby, it is essential to monitor your weight gain and ensure it remains within the recommended range for your body type. Your healthcare provider will guide you in maintaining a healthy weight and provide dietary recommendations to support your baby's growth.

Along with a growing belly and weight gain, you may experience other physical symptoms during pregnancy. Fatigue and morning sickness are common early on, but they usually subside as you enter the second trimester. Hormonal changes may also result in mood swings, tender breasts, and changes in skin pigmentation. Embrace these symptoms as part of the incredible process your body is undergoing and remember that they are temporary.

As your pregnancy progresses, you may encounter other physical changes such as back pain, swollen ankles, and stretch marks. These are normal and can be managed with proper self-care and support. Regular exercise, stretching, and wearing comfortable shoes can help alleviate discomfort. Additionally, maintaining a healthy diet and staying hydrated can reduce swelling and promote overall well-being.

It is essential to remember that every pregnancy is unique, and the physical changes and symptoms experienced can vary. If you have any concerns or questions, do not hesitate to reach out to your healthcare provider. They are your best resource for guidance and support throughout this transformative journey.

Embrace the physical changes and symptoms that come with motherhood, as they are a testament to the incredible process your body is undergoing to bring new life into the world. Take care of yourself, listen to your body, and enjoy this beautiful experience of becoming a first-time mom.

Emotional Changes and Mood Swings

Becoming a first-time mom is an incredibly beautiful and transformative experience, but it also comes with its fair share of emotional changes and mood swings. It's completely normal to feel a rollercoaster of emotions during this time, as your body adjusts to the hormonal fluctuations and the overwhelming responsibilities of caring for a new baby. In this subchapter, we will explore the various emotional changes and mood swings that new moms might experience, along with some practical tips to navigate through them.

One common emotional change that many new moms face is the "baby blues." These are characterized by feelings of sadness, anxiety, and irritability, usually occurring a few days after giving birth. The baby blues are caused by hormonal changes and the adjustment to the demands of motherhood. It's important to remember that these feelings are temporary and usually subside within a couple of weeks. However, if the symptoms persist or worsen, it could be a sign of postpartum depression, which requires professional help.

Mood swings are another common occurrence during the postpartum period. You may find yourself laughing one moment and crying the next, without any apparent reason. These mood swings are a result of hormonal changes, lack of sleep, and the stress of adapting to your new role as a mother. It's crucial to be patient with yourself and seek support from your loved ones. Remember, you're not alone in this journey, and there are many resources available to help you cope.

To manage emotional changes and mood swings effectively, it's important to prioritize self-care. Taking time for yourself, even if it's just a few minutes each day, can make a significant difference in your emotional well-being. Engage in activities that bring you joy and help you relax, such as reading, taking a bath, or practicing deep breathing exercises. Additionally, reaching out to other new moms or joining a support group can provide a sense of community and validation.

It's also essential to communicate your emotions and needs to your partner, family, or friends. Sharing your feelings and concerns can help alleviate the emotional burden and allow your loved ones to provide the support you require. Remember, seeking help is not a sign of weakness but a sign of strength and self-awareness.

In conclusion, emotional changes and mood swings are a normal part of the journey into motherhood. By understanding and accepting these changes, practicing self-care, and seeking support, you can navigate through this period with grace and resilience. Remember, you are doing an incredible job, and your emotions are valid. Embrace the journey and cherish the precious moments with your little one.

Prenatal Care and Doctor Visits

One of the most important aspects of a healthy pregnancy is receiving proper prenatal care. Regular doctor visits throughout your pregnancy will help ensure the well-being of both you and your baby. In this subchapter, we will discuss the significance of prenatal care and provide some valuable advice for new moms.

First and foremost, it is crucial to find a healthcare provider whom you trust and feel comfortable with. This may be an obstetrician-gynecologist (OB-GYN) or a certified nurse-midwife (CNM). They will be your primary contact during your pregnancy journey, guiding you through each stage and addressing any concerns you may have.

Prenatal care typically begins within the first few weeks after confirming your pregnancy, and continues until the birth of your baby. During these visits, your healthcare provider will monitor your overall health, perform routine screenings, and track the growth and development of your baby.

Regular doctor visits are essential for various reasons. They allow your healthcare provider to identify and address any potential complications or health issues early on. They also provide an opportunity for you to ask questions, seek advice, and gain reassurance about your pregnancy.

During these visits, you can expect to have your blood pressure checked, your weight monitored, and urine tested for any signs of infection or other complications. You will also undergo routine blood tests to check for conditions such as gestational diabetes and anemia. Additionally, your healthcare provider will listen to your baby's heartbeat and measure the size of your growing belly to ensure your baby is developing properly.

Remember, prenatal care is not only about physical health; it also encompasses emotional support. Your healthcare provider is there to address your concerns and provide guidance on maintaining a healthy lifestyle. They can offer advice on nutrition, exercise, and stress management, as well as prepare you for the upcoming childbirth experience.

As a new mom, it's crucial to prioritize your prenatal care and attend all scheduled doctor visits. By doing so, you are taking proactive steps to safeguard your well-being and the health of your baby. Don't hesitate to reach out to your healthcare provider if you have any questions or concerns between visits – they are there to support you every step of the way.

In summary, prenatal care and regular doctor visits are vital for a healthy and happy pregnancy. By investing in your prenatal care, you are ensuring the best possible start for your baby. Stay committed to your appointments, trust your healthcare provider, and embrace the journey of motherhood with confidence.

Building a Support System

One of the most important aspects of becoming a first-time mom is establishing a strong support system. As a new mom, you will face numerous challenges and uncertainties, and having a reliable network of support can make all the difference in your journey towards a happy baby and a fulfilling motherhood experience.

Your support system should ideally include a combination of family, friends, and professionals who can offer guidance, assistance, and emotional support. Let's take a closer look at some key elements of building a support system.

Family plays a crucial role in the first-time mom's journey. They can offer practical help, such as babysitting, cooking meals, or running errands, relieving some of the burdens of daily life. They can also provide invaluable emotional support, offering a listening ear or a shoulder to lean on during challenging times. Whether it's your partner, parents, or siblings, having family members who are actively involved and invested in your well-being can be a tremendous asset.

Friends are another essential part of your support system. Surrounding yourself with other new moms can provide a sense of camaraderie and shared experiences. Seek out local mom groups or join online communities dedicated to new moms. These networks will not only offer advice and tips but also provide a safe space for you to vent, share concerns, and celebrate milestones together.

Professional support is equally important. Seek out healthcare professionals who specialize in maternal and child health, such as obstetricians, pediatricians, and lactation consultants. These experts can provide valuable guidance on various aspects of your baby's well-being, from breastfeeding to sleep training. Additionally, consider enlisting the help of a postpartum doula or a therapist specializing in postpartum mental health to address any emotional challenges you may face.

Remember, building a support system is not a sign of weakness but a demonstration of strength and wisdom. No one can do it all alone, and it's essential to lean on others during this transformative period of your life.

By establishing a strong support system, you can navigate the ups and downs of motherhood with confidence and grace. Surround yourself with people who uplift and empower you, and don't hesitate to ask for help when you need it. Remember, you are not alone on this journey, and with the right support, you can provide your baby with a happy and nurturing environment.

Chapter 3: Creating a Safe and Comfortable Environment for Your Baby

Designing the Nursery

Creating a beautiful and functional nursery is an exciting part of preparing for your little one's arrival. As a new mom, you want everything to be perfect and safe for your baby. In this subchapter, we will guide you through the process of designing the nursery, helping you make the best choices for your baby's comfort and your peace of mind.

First and foremost, safety is paramount. When selecting furniture, choose pieces that meet the highest safety standards. Look for cribs with sturdy construction, slats that are properly spaced, and non-toxic finishes. Consider investing in a comfortable rocking chair or glider for those late-night feedings. Make sure to anchor any heavy furniture to the wall to prevent accidents.

Next, think about the layout of the nursery. Position the crib away from windows, blinds, and cords to avoid potential hazards. Keep the changing table close to the crib but ensure it is out of reach of your baby. Plan for ample storage space for all your baby's essentials, such as diapers, clothes, and toys.

When it comes to color schemes, opt for soothing and neutral tones. Soft pastels or earthy hues create a calm and peaceful environment. Avoid using strong, stimulating colors that might overstimulate your baby. Consider adding removable wall decals or artwork that can be easily changed as your baby grows.

Lighting is another crucial aspect of nursery design. Install blackout curtains or blinds to ensure a dark and sleep-friendly environment during nap times and bedtime. Consider using a combination of ambient lighting and task lighting. Soft, dimmable lights for nighttime feedings and a brighter light for diaper changes will be beneficial.

Additionally, think about incorporating elements that stimulate your baby's senses. Choose a soft, comfortable rug for tummy time or play. Hang a mobile above the crib with gentle, soothing music to entertain your baby. Consider adding a few books or soft toys that are age-appropriate for your little one.

Finally, don't forget to personalize the nursery with meaningful touches. Hang up family photos or create a gallery wall with adorable baby pictures. Consider adding a growth chart to track your baby's milestones over the years. These personal touches will make the nursery feel warm and inviting.

Designing the nursery is an exciting part of preparing for your baby's arrival. By prioritizing safety, creating a soothing environment, and incorporating personal touches, you will create a space that is both functional and beautiful. Enjoy this process and get ready to welcome your little one into a cozy, loving, and nurturing environment.

Essential Baby Gear and Equipment

As a new mom, preparing for the arrival of your baby can be both exciting and overwhelming. From choosing the perfect crib to deciding on the right stroller, there are countless baby gear options available in the market. In this subchapter, we will guide you through the essential baby gear and equipment that every new mom should consider.

. Crib and Mattress: Your baby will spend a significant amount of time in their crib, so it's important to choose a safe and comfortable one. Look for cribs that meet the safety standards and have adjustable mattress height options.

. Diapering Essentials: Diaper changing is an inevitable part of being mom. Make sure to have a changing table or a changing pad with a over, diapers (cloth or disposable), wipes, and diaper rash cream andy.

. Baby Monitor: A baby monitor allows you to keep an eye on your little one even when you are not in the same room. Choose one with ideo and audio capabilities for added peace of mind.

. Stroller and Car Seat: A reliable stroller and car seat are must-haves or any new mom. Look for a stroller that is lightweight, easy to maneuver, and has a sturdy build. Ensure that the car seat meets the afety standards and can be easily installed in your vehicle.

. Breastfeeding Essentials: If you plan to breastfeed, consider nvesting in a breast pump, nursing bras, nursing pads, and a nursing illow. These essentials will make your breastfeeding journey more omfortable and convenient.

6. Baby Carrier: A baby carrier allows you to keep your baby close while having your hands free. Opt for carriers that provide proper support to your baby's head, neck, and hips.

7. High Chair: As your baby starts transitioning to solid foods, a high chair becomes essential. Look for a high chair that is easy to clean, has safety straps, and adjustable height options.

8. Baby Bathing Supplies: Bath time can be a fun bonding experience. Ensure you have a baby bathtub, gentle baby soap, soft washcloths, and hooded towels to keep your baby clean and cozy.

Remember, while these essentials are important, every baby is unique and your needs may vary. It's essential to prioritize safety, comfort, and functionality when selecting baby gear and equipment. Don't hesitate to ask for recommendations from experienced moms or consult trusted sources to make informed decisions.

Baby-Proofing Your Home

Subchapter: Baby-Proofing Your Home

Congratulations, new moms! As you embark on this incredible journey of motherhood, ensuring the safety of your precious little one becomes a top priority. Baby-proofing your home is an essential step in creating a safe environment where your baby can explore, learn, and grow without unnecessary risks. In this subchapter, we will guide you through the process of baby-proofing your home to help you create a secure haven for your little bundle of joy.

1.   Identifying   Potential   Hazards: The first step in baby-proofing is to identify potential hazards within your home. From electrical outlets to sharp corners, it's crucial to assess every room and make a checklist of areas that need attention.

2.   Securing   Furniture   and   Appliances: Unstable furniture and appliances pose a significant risk to curious little explorers. We'll provide you with tips and tricks to secure heavy furniture, TVs, and other appliances to prevent accidents.

3.   Locking   Cabinets   and   Drawers: As your baby starts crawling and exploring, cabinets and drawers can become enticing targets. Learn about different types of locks and latches to keep those little hands out of harm's way.

4.   Covering   Electrical   Outlets: Electrical outlets are tempting for tiny fingers. Discover the various options available to cover and protect outlets, ensuring your baby's safety while maintaining functionality.

5.   Baby   Gates   and   Playpens: Baby gates and playpens are indispensable in creating safe spaces for

your little one, especially in areas like staircases or kitchens. We'll discuss how to choose the right ones and provide installation tips.

6.   Eliminating   Choking   Hazards: Babies tend to put everything in their mouths, making choking hazards a major concern. We'll help you identify and eliminate potential choking hazards, such as small toys, coins, and household items.

7.   Window   and   Door   Safety: Windows and doors can pose risks like falls or accidental entrapment. Explore various safety measures, including window guards, cordless blinds, and door stoppers to ensure your baby's well-being.

8.   Creating   a   Safe   Sleep   Environment: Your baby's sleep environment should be optimized for safety. We'll cover guidelines for crib safety, proper mattress fitting, and reducing the risk of Sudden Infant Death Syndrome (SIDS).

By following the guidance in this subchapter, you'll be able to transform your home into a secure space where your baby can thrive. Remember, baby-proofing is an ongoing process, as your little one grows and becomes more mobile. Stay vigilant, adapt to new challenges, and always prioritize safety. With a well-prepared home, you can confidently embrace the joys and wonders of motherhood, knowing that your baby is protected at every turn.

Establishing Routines and Schedules

As a new mom, one of the most important things you can do for yourself and your baby is to establish routines and schedules. A well-planned routine can bring a sense of order and predictability to your day, making it easier for you to navigate the challenges and joys of motherhood. In this subchapter, we will explore the benefits of routines and schedules and provide practical tips to help you create a harmonious daily rhythm for you and your little one.

Why are routines and schedules important for new moms? Firstly, they help babies feel secure and develop a sense of trust in their environment. By following a consistent routine, you can create a structured and comforting atmosphere that promotes your baby's emotional well-being. Secondly, routines can help regulate your baby's biological clock, enabling them to establish healthy sleep patterns and eat at regular intervals. This, in turn, can lead to better quality sleep for both you and your baby, reducing fatigue and enhancing your overall well-being.

Creating a routine may seem daunting at first, but remember that it can be flexible and adapted to your baby's needs. Start by establishing a consistent wake-up time and bedtime. Babies thrive on consistency, so try to stick to these times as closely as possible. Next, develop a feeding schedule that suits both you and your baby. Aim for regular intervals between feedings, but also be responsive to your baby's hunger cues. As your baby grows, you can gradually introduce solid foods and incorporate them into your routine.

In addition to sleep and feeding schedules, it's important to set aside time for play, tummy time, and bonding activities. Engage in age-appropriate games and sensory experiences to stimulate your baby's development. As your baby grows older, you can introduce a regular nap schedule and incorporate activities that encourage exploration and learning.

Remember, routines and schedules are not meant to be rigid or restrictive. They are tools to help you and your baby find a sense of balance and predictability in your day-to-day life. Be patient with yourself and your baby as you establish these routines, and be open to making adjustments along the way. As your baby grows and develops, their needs will change, and your routine will evolve accordingly.

In conclusion, establishing routines and schedules can greatly benefit new moms and their babies. By providing structure, predictability, and consistency, routines can promote emotional well-being, healthy sleep patterns, and overall family harmony. Embrace the process of developing a routine that works for you and your baby, and enjoy the journey of motherhood with a happy and contented little one by your side.

Chapter 4: The Miracle of Birth: Labor, Delivery, and the First Moments with Your Baby

Signs of Labor and When to Go to the Hospital

As a first-time mom, the prospect of going into labor can be both exciting and nerve-wracking. Understanding the signs of labor and knowing when to go to the hospital is essential for a smooth and stress-free birthing experience. In this subchapter, we will discuss the common signs that indicate labor is approaching and provide guidance on when it's time to head to the hospital.

One of the first signs that labor may be imminent is the onset of regular contractions. These contractions feel like intense menstrual cramps and usually start in the lower back and radiate to the front of the abdomen. As labor progresses, contractions become stronger, longer, and closer together. Timing your contractions will help you determine if you're in early labor or if it's time to call your healthcare provider.

Another sign to look out for is the breaking of the amniotic sac, commonly referred to as your water breaking. This can happen as a sudden gush or a slow trickle. If your water breaks, it's important to go to the hospital regardless of whether or not contractions have started, as this may increase the risk of infection.

Additionally, you may notice a bloody show, which is a small amount of blood-tinged mucus discharge. This occurs when the cervix begins to dilate and is often a sign that labor is imminent. However, keep in mind that the presence of a bloody show doesn't necessarily mean you need to rush to the hospital. It's essential to consider other signs and consult your healthcare provider for guidance.

Other signs of labor include a low, persistent backache, increased pelvic pressure, and a sensation that the baby has dropped lower into the pelvis. These signs indicate that your body is preparing for labor and should be taken into account when deciding when to go to the hospital.

When determining the right time to head to the hospital, it's crucial to communicate with your healthcare provider and follow their instructions. They will consider factors such as the frequency and intensity of contractions, your water breaking, and any other relevant signs. If you're uncertain, it's always better to err on the side of caution and seek medical advice.

Remember, every labor and delivery experience is unique, and it's important to trust your instincts. By being aware of the signs of labor and staying in close contact with your healthcare provider, you can ensure a safe and positive birthing experience for you and your baby.

Different Options for Labor and Delivery

When it comes to labor and delivery, every woman's journey is unique. As a first-time mom, it is important to be aware of the various options available to you, ensuring that you make informed decisions that align with your preferences and needs. In this subchapter, we will explore the different options for labor and delivery, empowering you to choose the best approach for a positive birthing experience.

1. Hospital Birth: The most common option, hospital births offer a safe and controlled environment with access to medical interventions if necessary. Obstetricians, nurses, and anesthesiologists are readily available to support you throughout the process.

2. Birth Center: Birth centers provide a more homely setting compared to hospitals. They are often run by midwives who focus on natural childbirth. These centers emphasize a calm and empowering environment, offering non-medicated pain relief techniques such as water births, massage, and breathing exercises.

3. Home Birth: For women seeking a truly intimate and familiar atmosphere, home birth is an option worth considering. With a certified midwife or doula present, you can experience labor and delivery surrounded by loved ones in the comfort of your own home. However, it is crucial to ensure that you have a backup plan in case of any emergencies.

4. Water Birth: Water births involve laboring and delivering in a specially designed birthing tub. This option can provide pain relief and relaxation, as the warm water helps ease discomfort. Many hospitals and birth centers offer this option, but it is essential to consult with your healthcare provider to determine if you are a suitable candidate.

5. Cesarean Section (C-Section): Sometimes, a C-section becomes necessary for various reasons, including complications or personal choice. This surgical procedure involves delivering the baby through an incision in the abdomen. While it may not be the preferred option for most women, it can be a life-saving procedure when needed.

Remember, the decision on where and how to give birth is entirely up to you. Take the time to research and explore the different options, discussing them with your healthcare provider, partner, and support system. Each woman's experience is unique, and what matters most is creating a safe and positive environment for you and your baby's arrival.

Whether you choose a hospital birth, birth center, home birth, water birth, or a C-section, the goal remains the same – a healthy and happy baby and a positive birthing experience for you as a new mom. Trust your instincts, gather information, and make choices that align with your desires and needs, ensuring that you feel empowered and supported throughout this incredible journey of motherhood.

Coping with Pain and Managing Labor

Labor and childbirth can be an overwhelming experience for first-time moms. The anticipation of pain and the fear of the unknown can make the whole process seem daunting. However, with the right knowledge and strategies, you can cope with the pain and manage labor effectively, ensuring a positive birthing experience for both you and your baby.

Understanding the Stages of Labor: Before delving into pain management techniques, it's crucial to have a basic understanding of the stages of labor. The first stage involves early labor, active labor, and transition, during which contractions become stronger and more frequent. The second stage is the pushing stage, where you work to bring your baby into the world. The third stage involves the delivery of the placenta.

Breathing and Relaxation Techniques: Learning and practicing breathing and relaxation techniques can significantly help reduce pain during labor. Techniques like deep breathing, visualization, and guided imagery can calm your mind, relax your body, and distract you from the pain. You can also try massage, warm showers, or using a birthing ball to find a comfortable position during contractions.

Pain Medication Options: If you find that the pain becomes too intense to manage through natural techniques, there are various pain medication options available. These include epidurals, which provide pain relief while allowing you to remain awake and actively participate in the birth. However, it's essential to discuss the pros and cons of each option with your healthcare provider to make an informed decision.

Supportive Birth Environment:
Creating a supportive birth environment can make a world of difference in managing labor pain. Surround yourself with a supportive birth team, including your partner, family members, or a doula, who can provide emotional and physical support throughout the process. Additionally, consider bringing comforting items from home, such as your favorite pillow or music playlist, to create a familiar and calming atmosphere.

Educate Yourself:
Knowledge is power, especially when it comes to managing labor pain. Attend childbirth education classes, read books, and seek information online to educate yourself about the birthing process. Knowing what to expect at each stage can help alleviate anxiety and allow you to make informed decisions about pain management techniques that align with your birth plan.

Remember, every woman's labor experience is unique, and what works for one may not work for another. The key is to stay open-minded, flexible, and communicate your needs and preferences with your healthcare provider. By incorporating these coping mechanisms and pain management strategies, you can approach labor with confidence, ultimately leading to a positive birthing experience for both you and your baby.

Bonding with Your Newborn

In the precious moments following the birth of your baby, a new chapter begins - the journey of bonding with your newborn. As a first-time mom, this connection is not only vital for your baby's development but also for your own emotional well-being. This subchapter explores the various ways you can strengthen the bond with your little one, creating a foundation of love and trust that will last a lifetime.

Skin-to-skin contact is a magical experience that promotes bonding from the very first moments. As soon as your baby is born, place them on your chest, allowing their warm body to feel your heartbeat and familiar scent. This immediate contact not only comforts the baby but also releases hormones in you, triggering feelings of deep attachment. Embrace this precious time together, gazing into each other's eyes and marveling at the miracle of life.

Breastfeeding, if possible, is another incredible opportunity to deepen the bond with your newborn. As you nourish your baby, you provide them with not only essential nutrients but also the comfort and security of being close to you. The intimate act of breastfeeding creates a profound bond, promoting a sense of safety and love. Remember, it's a learning process for both of you, so be patient and seek support if needed.

Cuddling and gentle touch are essential for newborns, as they crave physical contact. Whether you are holding your baby, giving them a gentle massage, or simply stroking their soft skin, these moments of touch create a sense of security and warmth. Your touch communicates love and affection, making your baby feel safe in your arms.

Don't underestimate the power of your voice. Talking, singing, and cooing to your baby not only soothes them but also helps develop their language and communication skills. Your voice is a source of comfort and familiarity, reminding them of the warmth and safety they experienced in the womb.

Finally, remember that bonding is not a one-time event but an ongoing process. As your baby grows, find joy in everyday activities like bath time, diaper changes, and playtime. Engage with them, respond to their cues, and be present in their world. These small moments of connection, filled with love and attentiveness, will build a strong and lasting bond between you and your little one.

As a new mom, the journey of bonding with your newborn is an incredible privilege. Cherish each moment, embrace the challenges, and let the love between you and your baby grow stronger with every passing day.

Chapter 5: Nourishing Your Baby: Breastfeeding, Bottle-Feeding, and Introducing Solid Foods

Benefits of Breastfeeding for Both Mom and Baby

Breastfeeding is a beautiful and natural way to nourish your baby, providing numerous benefits for both mom and baby. In this subchapter, we will explore the incredible advantages that breastfeeding offers to new moms and their precious little ones.

For   Baby:

Breast milk is often referred to as "liquid gold" for a good reason. It is the perfect source of nutrition for your baby, containing all the essential nutrients, antibodies, and enzymes needed for healthy growth and development. Here are some key benefits of breastfeeding for your baby:

1. Optimal Nutrition: Breast milk is uniquely tailored to meet the nutritional needs of your baby, ensuring they receive the ideal balance of carbohydrates, proteins, and fats.

2. Immune System Boost: Breast milk is rich in antibodies that help protect your baby against various illnesses, infections, and allergies. It boosts their immune system, reducing the risk of respiratory infections, gastrointestinal issues, and even chronic diseases later in life.

3. Cognitive Development: Studies have shown that breastfed babies tend to have higher IQ scores later in life. The essential fatty acids found in breast milk, such as DHA, play a crucial role in brain development.

4. Digestive Health: Breast milk is easily digested by your baby's delicate stomach, reducing the likelihood of constipation, diarrhea, and other digestive problems.

For   Mom:
Breastfeeding not only benefits your baby but also offers several advantages for you as a new mom. Here are some of the benefits you can experience:

1. Bonding and Emotional Connection: Breastfeeding creates a unique bond between you and your baby. The skin-to-skin contact, eye contact, and physical closeness during breastfeeding enhance the emotional connection between you both.

2. Postpartum Weight Loss: Breastfeeding can help you shed those extra pounds gained during pregnancy. It burns calories and triggers the release of hormones that promote weight loss.

3. Reduced Risk of Postpartum Depression: Breastfeeding stimulates the release of oxytocin, a hormone known as the "love hormone." This hormone promotes feelings of relaxation, happiness, and decreases the risk of postpartum depression.

4. Reduced Risk of Breast and Ovarian Cancer: Research suggests that breastfeeding can reduce the risk of breast and ovarian cancer in mothers. The longer you breastfeed, the more protection you may gain.

In conclusion, breastfeeding is a win-win situation for both mom and baby. It provides your baby with optimal nutrition, boosts their immune system, and supports their overall development. For moms, breastfeeding enhances the emotional connection with their baby, aids in postpartum weight loss, reduces the risk of postpartum depression, and offers long-term health benefits. Embrace the precious moments of breastfeeding, knowing that you are providing the best for your baby while reaping the rewards yourself.

Overcoming Breastfeeding Challenges

Breastfeeding is a beautiful and natural way to nourish your baby while creating a special bond between you and your little one. However, it is not always a smooth journey for new moms. Many women face challenges along the way that can make breastfeeding seem like an uphill battle. But fear not, dear new moms, for in this chapter, we will discuss common breastfeeding challenges and provide you with practical tips and advice to help you overcome them.

One of the most common challenges new moms face is difficulty with latching. Proper positioning and latching are crucial for successful breastfeeding. We will guide you through different techniques, such as the "laid-back" and "cross-cradle" positions, to ensure your baby can latch correctly and comfortably.

Another challenge that may arise is low milk supply. It is important to understand that this doesn't necessarily mean you are not producing enough milk. We will explore the factors that can affect milk production, such as stress and inadequate nutrition, and offer solutions to boost your milk supply naturally.

Sore and cracked nipples are another hurdle that many new moms encounter. We will explain the causes behind nipple pain and provide you with tips on how to prevent and treat this discomfort. From proper latch techniques to using lanolin cream, we will help you find relief and continue your breastfeeding journey with ease.

Breast engorgement, plugged ducts, and mastitis can also pose challenges for new moms. We will explain the causes and symptoms of these conditions and provide you with strategies to prevent and alleviate them. From warm compresses to gentle massage techniques you will learn how to navigate these hurdles and keep your breastfeeding experience positive and enjoyable.

Lastly, we will address the emotional challenges that can accompany breastfeeding. Many new moms feel overwhelmed, frustrated, or even guilty if they encounter difficulties. We will offer guidance on seeking support from lactation consultants or joining breastfeeding support groups. You are not alone in this journey, and with the right support system, you can overcome any obstacle that comes your way.

Breastfeeding is a personal and unique experience for every new mom. While it can be challenging at times, with the right knowledge and support, you can overcome any breastfeeding obstacle you face. Remember, you are providing your baby with the best nourishment and creating an unbreakable bond. By arming yourself with the information and tips provided in this chapter, you will be well-prepared to conquer any breastfeeding challenge that comes your way.

Bottle-Feeding: Choosing the Right Formula and Equipment

As a new mom, one of the decisions you will face is whether to breastfeed or bottle-feed your baby. While breastfeeding is often recommended due to its numerous benefits, it may not always be feasible option for every mother. If you have decided to bottle-feed your baby, it is essential to choose the right formula and equipment to ensure your little one's health and happiness.

Choosing the right formula is crucial as it will provide the necessary nutrients for your baby's growth and development. There are various types of formulas available, such as cow's milk-based, soy-based, and hypoallergenic formulas. It is essential to consult with your pediatrician to determine the best formula for your baby's individual needs. Factors like any allergies, digestive issues, or special dietary requirements should be taken into consideration when selecting the formula.

When it comes to equipment, there are a few essentials you will need to ensure a smooth bottle-feeding experience. Firstly, you will need bottles and nipples. Opt for bottles that are easy to clean and sterilize and consider purchasing a few different types of nipples to see which one your baby prefers. Bottle brushes and sterilizers are also essential for maintaining cleanliness and hygiene.

Additionally, investing in a bottle warmer can make feeding time more convenient, especially during those late-night feedings when you want to quickly warm a bottle without having to use the stove or microwave. It is also advisable to have a bottle drying rack to keep everything organized and allow bottles to air dry properly.

When it comes to feeding your baby, it is important to establish a routine and follow proper guidelines for preparing and storing formula. Always read the instructions on the formula packaging carefully and follow them precisely. Prepare the formula in a clean and sanitized environment, and discard any unused formula within the recommended time frame.

Remember, bottle-feeding can be a bonding experience for you and your baby, just like breastfeeding. Make sure to hold your baby close, maintain eye contact, and give them plenty of love and attention during feeding times. This will help create a nurturing and comforting environment for your little one.

In conclusion, choosing the right formula and equipment for bottle-feeding is crucial for your baby's well-being. Consult with your pediatrician, research different options, and consider your baby's specific needs when making these choices. With the right formula and equipment, bottle-feeding can be a joyful and fulfilling experience for both you and your baby.

Introducing Solid Foods to Your Baby

As a new mom, you may find yourself both excited and nervous about the prospect of introducing solid foods to your baby. This subchapter aims to guide you through this important milestone in your little one's development.

When it comes to starting solids, it's essential to remember that every baby is different. While some may be ready as early as four months, others might not show interest until six months or even later. Always consult with your pediatrician to ensure your baby is developmentally ready and has the necessary physical skills to handle solid foods.

One of the first signs of readiness is when your baby can hold their head up independently. This is crucial as they need to be sitting upright to eat solids safely. Other signs include increased curiosity in food, the ability to close their lips around a spoon, and the diminishing of the tongue-thrust reflex.

When choosing foods to introduce, begin with single-ingredient, pureed fruits or vegetables. Some popular first foods include mashed bananas, pureed sweet potatoes, or avocado. Start with small amounts, gradually increasing the quantity as your baby gets accustomed to new textures and tastes.

It's important to introduce one new food at a time, allowing several days before introducing another. This helps you identify any potential allergies or sensitivities. Signs of an allergic reaction may include rashes, vomiting, or diarrhea. If you suspect an allergy, contact your pediatrician immediately.

Breast milk or formula should still be the primary source of nutrition during the first year. Solid foods are meant to complement, not replace, milk. As your baby grows, introduce a variety of foods, including grains, proteins, and dairy products. Remember to avoid honey, cow's milk, and any choking hazards such as nuts or popcorn.

Mealtime should be a positive and enjoyable experience for both you and your baby. Sit your little one in a high chair and engage them in conversation while feeding. Let them explore different tastes and textures, even if they initially make a mess. This helps them develop their fine motor skills and fosters a healthy relationship with food.

Remember, every baby is unique, and some may take longer to adjust to solids than others. Be patient and trust your instincts as a mom. With time, your baby will become a confident eater, exploring a wide range of nutritious and delicious foods.

Chapter 6: Developmental Milestones: Tracking Your Baby's Growth and Development

Understanding Baby's Physical and Cognitive Development

Being a new mom is an exhilarating and overwhelming experience. As you embark on this beautiful journey of motherhood, it is vital to understand your baby's physical and cognitive development. By gaining insight into these aspects, you can provide the best care and support for your little one's growth and overall well-being.

Physical development refers to the changes in a baby's body and motor skills. From the moment your baby is born, they start discovering their surroundings through their senses. As a new mom, it is essential to stimulate their senses by providing them with a safe environment rich in visual, auditory, and tactile experiences. Engaging with your baby through gentle touch, colorful toys, and soothing sounds helps in fostering their physical development.

During the first year, your baby's motor skills progress at a remarkable pace. From the early days of grasping your finger to eventually crawling and walking, each milestone is a testament to their physical growth. Encourage your little one's development by providing ample tummy time to strengthen their muscles, offering age-appropriate toys to enhance coordination, and celebrating their achievements along the way.

Cognitive development, on the other hand, focuses on your baby's mental processes, including their ability to think, learn, and understand the world around them. Babies are like sponges, absorbing information and making sense of it through observation and exploration. As a new mom, you play a crucial role in stimulating your baby's cognitive development. Engage in activities that encourage curiosity, such as reading books, singing songs, and playing peek-a-boo. These interactions help develop their memory, attention span, and problem-solving skills.

Understanding your baby's physical and cognitive development also means being aware of potential milestones and red flags. While each child is unique and develops at their own pace, it is important to keep an eye out for any significant delays or concerns. Regular check-ups with your pediatrician allow you to track your baby's growth and identify any potential issues early on.

Remember, being a new mom is a journey of discovery for both you and your baby. Embrace the joy and challenges that come with understanding your baby's physical and cognitive development. By nurturing their growth and providing a loving environment, you lay a strong foundation for a happy and healthy future.

Monitoring Motor Skills and Communication Milestones

As a new mom, it's perfectly natural to have concerns about your baby's development. Every milestone, from their first smile to their first steps, is a cause for celebration and a sign that your little one is growing and thriving. In this subchapter, we will explore the importance of monitoring your baby's motor skills and communication milestones, and provide you with the tools and knowledge to track their progress effectively.

Motor skills refer to your baby's ability to use their muscles and coordinate their movements. From the moment they enter this world, they are constantly developing and refining these skills. By monitoring their motor milestones, you can gain insight into their overall growth and ensure that they are hitting their developmental markers.

One of the essential motor milestones to observe is their ability to hold their head up. This skill typically develops around 3 to 4 months of age. As your baby grows, you can also track their progress in rolling over, sitting up, crawling, and ultimately walking. These milestones vary from baby to baby, so it's crucial to remember that each child develops at their own pace. However, if you notice any significant delays or concerns, it's always best to consult with your pediatrician for further guidance and support.

Communication milestones are equally important to monitor. From cooing and babbling to saying their first words, your baby's ability to communicate is essential for their overall development. Even before they can speak, they will use nonverbal cues, such as gestures and facial expressions, to convey their needs and emotions. Paying attention to these milestones will help you better understand your baby's wants and needs and foster early language development.

In this subchapter, we will provide you with a comprehensive checklist of motor skills and communication milestones to track. We will also offer tips and activities to support your baby's development in these areas. Remember, every baby is unique, and progress may vary. However, by monitoring these milestones, you can ensure that your little one is reaching their full potential and provide them with the necessary support along the way.

Monitoring motor skills and communication milestones is an exciting journey that allows you to witness your baby's growth firsthand. By staying informed and attentive, you can give your little one the best start in life and nurture their development in a loving and supportive environment.

Encouraging Sensory and Social Development

As a new mom, you might find yourself wondering how you can support your baby's sensory and social development during these crucial early months. Rest assured, there are plenty of simple and enjoyable activities you can incorporate into your daily routine to help your little one thrive in these areas.

Sensory development refers to how your baby processes information through their senses. By stimulating their senses, you are helping them build neural connections and develop crucial skills for later life. One way to encourage sensory development is through playtime. Engage your baby with toys of various textures, colors, and sounds. Allow them to explore different objects with their hands, mouth, and eyes. This will not only stimulate their senses but also enhance their hand eye coordination.

Another great way to encourage sensory development is through sensory play. Set up a safe and supervised area where your baby can explore different materials like water, sand, or even cooked pasta. This will provide them with a rich sensory experience, allowing them to discover their world through touch, smell, and taste.

In addition to sensory development, social development is equally important for your baby's overall growth. Babies learn about the world around them through social interactions, so it's crucial to provide them with ample opportunities to engage with others. Spend quality time talking, singing, and reading to your baby. This not only fosters language development but also builds a strong emotional bond between you and your little one.

Playdates and baby groups are also excellent ways to encourage social development. By exposing your baby to different people and environments, they will learn to interact with others and develop important social skills such as sharing, taking turns, and empathy. These experiences will lay a solid foundation for their future relationships and interactions.

Remember, every baby develops at their own pace, so be patient and enjoy the journey. Encouraging sensory and social development doesn't have to be complicated or time-consuming. By incorporating these simple activities into your daily routine, you will be providing your baby with the tools they need to explore and thrive in their world.

Recognizing and Addressing Developmental Delays

As a new mom, one of the most important aspects of your baby's growth and development is their reaching key milestones. These milestones include physical, cognitive, and social-emotional skills tha your child should achieve within a certain timeframe. However, it's essential to remember that every child is unique and may develop a their own pace. Nevertheless, it is crucial to be aware of potentia developmental delays and take appropriate action when necessary.

Identifying developmental delays can be challenging, especially for first-time moms. In this subchapter, we will explore some common signs that may indicate your baby is experiencing a delay in their development. It is important to emphasize that this information is for general guidance only. Always consult with your pediatrician or healthcare provider for professional advice.

Physical developmental delays may manifest in areas such as motor skills, coordination, or muscle strength. For example, if your baby is not rolling over, sitting up, crawling, or walking within the expected age range, it might be a reason for concern. Cognitive delays may be noticed if your baby is not making eye contact, responding to their name, or showing curiosity about their surroundings.

Social-emotional developmental delays can also be observed in infants. For instance, if your baby is not smiling, making babbling sounds, or engaging in social interactions, it could be an indicator of a delay Additionally, if your baby is not showing an interest in playing with toys or imitating actions, further investigation may be necessary.

If you notice any potential signs of developmental delays, it is crucia to take action promptly. Early intervention can make a significant difference in your child's development. Schedule an appointment with your pediatrician to discuss your concerns and seek a professional assessment.

Remember, not every delay is cause for alarm, and your pediatrician will provide expert guidance tailored to your baby's unique situation. In some cases, your child may simply need a little extra time to reach their milestones, while others may require early intervention services, such as physical or occupational therapy.

As a new mom, it is important to stay informed and proactive in recognizing and addressing developmental delays. By being attentive and seeking professional advice, you can ensure your baby receives the support they need to thrive.

Chapter 7: Keeping Your Baby Healthy: Vaccinations, Common Illnesses, and Doctor Visits

Importance of Vaccinations and Immunizations

Subchapter: Importance of Vaccinations and Immunizations

Introduction:

As a new mom, you have embarked on a remarkable journey filled with love, joy, and the desire to give your baby the best start in life. One crucial aspect of ensuring your baby's well-being is understanding the importance of vaccinations and immunizations. In this subchapter, we will explore why these medical interventions are vital for your little one's health and the broader community.

Protecting Your Baby:

Vaccinations and immunizations play a pivotal role in safeguarding your baby from potentially life-threatening diseases. These preventive measures stimulate your baby's immune system to create defenses against harmful pathogens. By receiving vaccinations, your baby can develop immunity to a range of diseases, including measles, mumps, rubella, polio, whooping cough, and more. This immunity helps your baby fight off infections and reduces the risk of severe illness or even death.

Community Health:

Vaccinations not only protect your baby but also contribute to the overall health of the community. By ensuring your baby receives the recommended vaccinations, you are helping to create a shield of protection around those who cannot be vaccinated, such as individuals with compromised immune systems or allergies. This concept, known as herd immunity, helps prevent the spread of diseases and protects vulnerable populations.

Preventing Outbreaks:

Vaccinations are key in preventing disease outbreaks. Diseases that were once common, such as measles or polio, have been largely eradicated in many parts of the world due to successful vaccination programs. However, without widespread immunization, there is a risk of these diseases resurging and causing outbreaks. By vaccinating your baby, you are actively participating in the global effort to eliminate infectious diseases and create a safer environment for everyone.

Long-Term Health Benefits:

Vaccinations not only provide immediate protection but also offer long-term health benefits for your child. Immunizations can prevent complications and long-lasting health issues associated with certain diseases. For instance, the hepatitis B vaccine can prevent liver cancer, and the human papillomavirus (HPV) vaccine reduces the risk of cervical cancer later in life. By staying up-to-date with your baby's vaccinations, you are investing in their lifelong well-being.

Conclusion:

In this subchapter, we have highlighted the importance of vaccinations and immunizations for new moms and their babies. By ensuring your little one receives the recommended vaccines, you are not only protecting them from dangerous diseases but also contributing to the health of the community. Vaccinations offer immediate and long-term benefits for your baby, helping them stay healthy and thrive. As a responsible and caring parent, staying informed about vaccination schedules and discussing any concerns with your healthcare provider is crucial. Remember, by prioritizing your baby's immunizations, you are playing an essential role in building a healthier future for your child and the broader society.

Common Illnesses in Infants and How to Handle Them

As a new mom, one of your top priorities is keeping your baby healthy and safe. However, it's inevitable that your little one will sometimes fall ill. Understanding the most common illnesses in infants and knowing how to handle them can help ease your worries and ensure your baby receives the best care. In this subchapter, we will discuss some of the most frequent ailments newborns and infants experience, along with practical tips on how to deal with them.

. Common Cold: Infants are susceptible to colds, especially during their first year. Symptoms may include a runny or stuffy nose, cough, mild fever, and fussiness. Ensure your baby stays hydrated, use a nasal aspirator to clear their nose, and provide comfort through gentle cuddling and soothing techniques.

. Fever: Fever is often a sign that your baby's body is fighting off an infection. Use a reliable thermometer to monitor their temperature and consult a pediatrician if it exceeds 100.4°F (38°C). Dress your baby in lightweight clothing, offer plenty of fluids, and administer fever-reducing medication if advised by a healthcare professional.

. Diarrhea: Diarrhea can lead to dehydration in infants. Keep an eye on your baby's diaper output and consult a doctor if they have watery stools more frequently than usual. Offer fluids to prevent dehydration and continue breastfeeding or formula feeding.

. Rashes: Common rashes in infants include diaper rash, heat rash, and eczema. Keep your baby's skin clean and dry, change diapers frequently, and apply a diaper rash cream as needed. For other rashes, consult a pediatrician for appropriate treatment options.

5. Ear Infections: Ear infections can cause discomfort and fussiness in infants. Watch out for signs such as tugging at the ears, irritability, and difficulty sleeping. If you suspect an ear infection, seek medical advice. To alleviate pain, use a warm compress and keep your baby in an upright position.

Remember, it's crucial to consult a healthcare professional for an accurate diagnosis and personalized advice. Trust your instincts as a mom, and don't hesitate to seek medical guidance whenever necessary. By staying informed and following these practical tips, you will gain confidence in handling common illnesses and providing the best care for your baby's well-being.

Whether you're a first-time mom or have experienced motherhood before, this subchapter offers valuable insights into recognizing and managing the common illnesses your infant may encounter. By being prepared and proactive, you can ensure your little one stays happy and healthy throughout their early years.

Regular Check-ups with Your Baby's Pediatrician

As a new mom, one of the most important things you can do to ensure the health and well-being of your baby is to schedule regular check-ups with their pediatrician. These check-ups are vital for monitoring your baby's growth and development, as well as detecting any potential health issues early on. In this subchapter, we will discuss the importance of regular check-ups and provide you with some tips to make the most out of these visits.

Why are regular check-ups important?

Regular check-ups with your baby's pediatrician are not only essential for their physical health but also for their mental and emotional well-being. During these visits, the pediatrician will assess your baby's growth, check their vital signs, and conduct various screenings and assessments to ensure that they are meeting their developmental milestones.

Additionally, regular check-ups allow the pediatrician to address any concerns or questions you may have as a new mom. They can provide guidance on breastfeeding, formula feeding, sleep patterns, and other aspects of your baby's care. These visits also offer an opportunity for you to discuss any behavioral or emotional issues you may have noticed in your little one.

Making the most out of check-ups

To make the most out of your baby's check-ups, it's important to come prepared. Before the appointment, write down any questions or concerns you have so that you don't forget to discuss them. Keep a record of your baby's feeding and sleeping patterns, as well as any changes in their behavior or health since the last visit.

During the check-up, don't hesitate to ask questions and seek clarification on any instructions or recommendations given by the pediatrician. Remember, they are there to help and support you in your journey as a new mom.

It's also important to stay up-to-date with your baby's immunizations. Vaccines are a crucial part of keeping your baby healthy and protected from potentially life-threatening diseases. Your pediatrician will provide you with a vaccination schedule, and it's essential to follow it diligently.

Lastly, don't forget to establish a good rapport with your baby's pediatrician. Building a trusting relationship with your healthcare provider is vital for open communication and receiving the best care for your little one.

In conclusion, regular check-ups with your baby's pediatrician are crucial for their overall health and well-being. These visits provide an opportunity for growth monitoring, developmental assessments, and addressing any concerns you may have as a new mom. By staying proactive and engaged during these visits, you can ensure the optimal care and happiness of your baby.

Creating a Healthy Environment for Your Baby

As a new mom, there is nothing more important than the health and well-being of your precious little one. Creating a healthy environment for your baby is crucial for their growth and development. In this subchapter, we will explore various aspects of maintaining a safe and nurturing space for your bundle of joy.

First and foremost, ensuring cleanliness is paramount. Regularly clean and disinfect your baby's living areas, including their nursery, playpen, and toys. Use baby-friendly cleaning products that are free from harsh chemicals to minimize any potential harm to your baby's sensitive skin and respiratory system.

Proper ventilation is also essential in maintaining a healthy environment. Open windows or use air purifiers to improve air circulation and reduce indoor air pollutants. Fresh air not only keeps your baby's lungs healthy but also promotes better sleep and overall well-being.

Maintaining an optimal temperature is crucial for your baby's comfort and safety. Avoid overheating by dressing your baby in light, breathable clothing during warmer months and using a fan or air conditioner. In colder months, layer their clothing and keep the room temperature between 68-72 degrees Fahrenheit to prevent them from getting too cold.

Creating a peaceful and soothing atmosphere is equally important. Play soft, calming music or use white noise machines to help your baby relax and sleep better. Avoid exposure to loud noises or sudden bursts of sound that may startle them.

When it comes to your baby's sleep environment, prioritize safety Ensure that their crib meets safety standards and is free from any loose bedding, pillows, or stuffed animals that could pose a suffocation risk Place your baby on their back to sleep to reduce the risk of Sudden Infant Death Syndrome (SIDS).

Maintaining a healthy environment extends beyond the physical aspects. Emphasize emotional well-being by surrounding your baby with love and positive energy. Engage in regular bonding activities such as cuddling, singing, and talking to your baby. Respond promptly to their needs, as this fosters a sense of security and trust.

Finally, make sure to take care of your own well-being. As a new mom it is easy to neglect self-care, but remember that your baby needs a healthy and happy caregiver. Take breaks when needed, eat nutritious meals, and get enough rest to maintain your own physical and mental health.

Creating a healthy environment for your baby is a lifelong commitment. By prioritizing cleanliness, ventilation, temperature control, safety, emotional well-being, and self-care, you are setting the foundation for a happy and thriving baby. Remember, every small effort you make contributes to your baby's overall health and happiness.

Chapter 8: Sleep Solutions: Helping Your Baby Establish Healthy Sleep Habits

Understanding Newborn Sleep Patterns

Sleep is a crucial aspect of a newborn's development, and as a new mom, it's essential to understand their sleep patterns. In this subchapter, we will delve into the fascinating world of newborn sleep and explore the various sleep patterns that your little one may exhibit.

Newborns have an irregular sleep pattern, and it is completely normal for them to sleep for short periods throughout the day and night. They typically sleep for about 16 to 20 hours a day, with each sleep session lasting anywhere from a few minutes to a few hours. It's important to remember that their sleep is divided into cycles, consisting of active sleep and quiet sleep.

During active sleep, your baby may make various movements, twitch, and even cry. This is when they are dreaming and experiencing rapid eye movement (REM) sleep. In contrast, quiet sleep is characterized by stillness, slower breathing, and deeper sleep. Understanding these sleep cycles will help you recognize when your baby is in a light or deep sleep, enabling you to respond accordingly to their needs.

As a new mom, it's crucial to establish healthy sleep habits for your newborn. Encouraging a consistent sleep routine can help regulate their sleep patterns and promote better sleep. Creating a calm and soothing environment during bedtime, such as dimming the lights and playing soft lullabies, can signal to your baby that it's time to sleep.

While it's tempting to keep your newborn awake during the day in hopes of a longer stretch of sleep at night, overstimulation can lead to fussiness and difficulty falling asleep. Instead, provide gentle stimulation during the day, such as talking or singing softly, and allow them to nap as needed. This will help prevent overtiredness, which can make it harder for your baby to settle down at bedtime.

In the first few months, your baby's sleep patterns will gradually become more organized. They will start sleeping for longer stretches at night, and their daytime naps will become more predictable. However, it's important to remember that every baby is unique, and their sleep patterns may vary. Be patient and flexible as you navigate your baby's sleep journey, seeking guidance when needed.

Understanding your newborn's sleep patterns will not only help you establish a healthy routine but also enable you to respond promptly to their needs. By providing a nurturing sleep environment and being attuned to your baby's cues, you can help them develop healthy sleep habits that will set the foundation for a happy and well-rested baby.

In the next chapter, we will explore practical tips and strategies for helping your newborn sleep through the night and establish a peaceful bedtime routine.

Creating a Safe and Comfortable Sleep Environment

As a new mom, one of the most important things you can do for your baby is to provide a safe and comfortable sleep environment. A good night's sleep is crucial for your little one's development and overall well-being. In this subchapter, we will explore some essential tips and guidelines to ensure that your baby sleeps soundly and securely.

First and foremost, it is vital to choose the right crib for your baby. Look for a crib that meets the safety standards set by the Consumer Product Safety Commission (CPSC). Ensure that the slats are no more than 2 3/8 inches apart to prevent your baby's head from getting stuck. Avoid using drop-side cribs, as they have been deemed unsafe. Additionally, make sure the mattress fits snugly in the crib, leaving no gaps between the mattress and the crib's sides.

To reduce the risk of sudden infant death syndrome (SIDS), it is recommended that you place your baby on their back to sleep. This sleeping position has been proven to be the safest. Avoid using pillows, blankets, or stuffed animals in the crib, as they can pose suffocation hazards. Instead, dress your baby in appropriate sleepwear to keep them warm.

Maintaining a suitable room temperature is also crucial for your baby's comfort. The ideal temperature for a baby's room is between 68 and 72 degrees Fahrenheit. Use a room thermometer to monitor the temperature and adjust accordingly. To prevent overheating, dress your baby in light, breathable clothing and avoid heavy blankets.

Creating a soothing and calm sleep environment can also help your baby fall asleep more easily. Consider using blackout curtains to block out any external light, which can disrupt sleep. Use a white noise machine or a fan to create a gentle, consistent sound that mimics the womb environment, providing a sense of comfort for your baby.

Regularly check the crib for any loose or damaged parts that could potentially harm your baby. Ensure that the crib is placed away from any cords or blinds that could pose a strangulation risk. Install baby gates at the top and bottom of stairs to prevent falls.

By following these guidelines and creating a safe and comfortable sleep environment, you can ensure that your baby gets the restful sleep they need for a happy and healthy development. Remember, a well-rested baby is a happy baby, and a well-rested mom is a happy mom!

Establishing Bedtime Routines and Sleep Training Methods

One of the biggest challenges new moms face is ensuring their little ones get enough sleep. Sleep is crucial for a baby's growth and development, and it also helps moms get the rest they need. In this subchapter, we will explore effective bedtime routines and sleep training methods that will help you and your baby establish healthy sleep patterns.

Bedtime routines are essential in signaling to your baby that it's time to wind down and prepare for sleep. Consistency is key when establishing these routines. Start by creating a calm and soothing environment by dimming the lights and playing soft music. A warm bath can also help relax your baby before bed. Follow this with a gentle massage using baby-safe oils or lotions. Incorporate a quiet activity such as reading a bedtime story or singing a lullaby. These activities will help create a positive association with sleep.

Sleep training is a method often used to teach babies to fall asleep independently and self-soothe. One popular approach is the Ferber method, where you gradually increase the amount of time between checking on your baby when they cry. Another method is the "pick up, put down" technique, where you pick up your baby when they cry but put them back down once they have calmed down. It's important to note that sleep training methods should be adjusted to suit your baby's temperament and age.

When implementing sleep training, it's important to remain patient and consistent. It may take a few nights for your baby to adjust, but with time, they will learn to fall asleep on their own. Remember, each baby is unique, and what works for one may not work for another. Be open to trying different techniques until you find what works best for you and your little one.

In addition to bedtime routines and sleep training, it's crucial to create a conducive sleep environment. Ensure the room is dark, quiet, and at a comfortable temperature. Use a crib or bassinet that meets safety standards and is free from any potential hazards. Consider using swaddles or sleep sacks to provide a cozy and secure feeling for your baby.

By establishing consistent bedtime routines, implementing appropriate sleep training methods, and creating a soothing sleep environment, you can help your baby develop healthy sleep habits. Remember, this process takes time, so be patient and adaptable. With your love and support, your little one will be on their way to peaceful nights and happy days.

Managing Sleep Regression and Transitions

As a new mom, one of the most challenging aspects of parenting is dealing with sleep regression and transitions. Just when you thought you had established a sleep routine for your little one, a regression hits, leaving you feeling exhausted and frustrated. But fear not! With the right strategies and a little patience, you can navigate through these sleep disruptions and ensure a happy baby.

Sleep regression typically occurs at specific developmental stages, such as around four months, eight months, and one year. During these times, your baby's sleep patterns may become disrupted, and they may struggle to fall asleep or stay asleep. It's important to remember that sleep regressions are temporary and are often signs of cognitive and physical development. Understanding this can bring you some reassurance during these trying times.

To manage sleep regression, it's crucial to establish a consistent and soothing bedtime routine. A predictable routine helps signal to your baby that it's time to wind down and prepare for sleep. This may include activities like a warm bath, gentle massage, reading a bedtime story, and dimming the lights. Stick to this routine even during regressions, as it will help your baby feel secure and calm.

During sleep regressions, it's also essential to be patient and flexible. Your baby may require extra comfort and reassurance during this time, so be prepared to offer more cuddles, rocking, or soothing techniques. Remember that this phase is temporary, and your little one will eventually return to their regular sleep patterns.

Transitions, such as moving from a crib to a toddler bed or transitioning from co-sleeping to a separate room, can also disrupt your baby's sleep. To ease these transitions, ensure a safe and comfortable sleep environment. Gradually introduce the changes, allowing your baby to adjust at their own pace. Offer familiar comfort objects like a favorite stuffed animal or blanket to provide a sense of security during these transitions.

Additionally, maintaining a consistent sleep schedule can help your baby adjust to new sleeping arrangements. Stick to regular nap times and bedtime routines to provide a sense of stability. Patience and consistency are key during these transitions, as it may take some time for your baby to adapt to the changes.

Remember, every baby is different, and what works for one may not work for another. Trust your instincts and be open to trying different techniques until you find what works best for your little one. With time, patience, and a little bit of trial and error, you'll conquer sleep regressions and transitions, ensuring a happy and well-rested baby.

Chapter 9: Balancing Motherhood: Taking Care of Yourself while Caring for Your Baby

Self-Care for New Moms

Becoming a mother for the first time is a beautiful and transformative experience. It brings immense joy and fulfillment but also comes with its fair share of challenges and adjustments. As a new mom, your focus naturally shifts towards your precious little one, and it's easy to neglect your own well-being in the process. However, taking care of yourself is crucial for your overall happiness and ability to care for your baby. This subchapter will guide you through the importance of self-care and provide practical tips to help you navigate this new chapter with confidence.

Self-care is not selfish; it's a necessity. Taking care of your physical, mental, and emotional well-being is essential for your own happiness and the well-being of your baby. Prioritizing self-care as a new mom can be challenging, but it's not impossible. Start by carving out small pockets of time for yourself each day. Whether it's a relaxing bubble bath, catching up on your favorite TV show, or simply taking a walk in the fresh air, these moments can do wonders for your mental and emotional state.

Physical self-care is equally crucial. Ensure you are getting enough rest by taking short naps when your baby sleeps. Make nutritious meals a priority, as a well-nourished body will provide you with the energy you need to care for your baby. Engage in gentle exercises or postnatal yoga to heal your body and boost your mood.

Emotional self-care is often overlooked but is vital for maintaining a healthy mindset. Seek support from your partner, family, and friends.

Join a new moms' support group or online community where you can share your experiences, ask questions, and find solace in the company of others going through similar situations. Don't hesitate to ask for help when needed; remember, you are not alone in this journey.

Remember to treat yourself with love and kindness. Celebrate the small victories and milestones, and don't be too hard on yourself when things don't go as planned. Practice self-compassion and remind yourself that you are doing your best.

In conclusion, self-care for new moms is a vital aspect of maintaining a healthy and happy life for both you and your baby. By prioritizing your physical, mental, and emotional well-being, you will be better equipped to handle the challenges that come with motherhood. Embrace self-care as an essential part of your routine, and remember that taking care of yourself is not only a gift to yourself but also to your baby.

Managing Postpartum Emotions and Mental Health

Becoming a new mom is an exciting and joyous experience, but it can also bring a rollercoaster of emotions. It's important to remember that feeling overwhelmed, anxious, or even sad after giving birth is completely normal. The postpartum period is a time of significant hormonal changes, physical recovery, and adjustment to a new role, which can all contribute to fluctuating emotions.

One of the first steps in managing postpartum emotions and mental health is recognizing and accepting that it's okay to feel a wide range of emotions. Many new moms put pressure on themselves to be happy and ecstatic all the time, but it's important to understand that it's natural to experience a mix of emotions during this time. It's crucial to give yourself permission to feel and process these emotions without judgment.

Self-care is another essential aspect of managing postpartum emotions. As a new mom, it's easy to prioritize the needs of your baby and neglect your own well-being. However, taking care of yourself physically and emotionally is crucial for your overall mental health. Make sure to get adequate rest, eat nutritious meals, and engage in activities that bring you joy. Even small acts of self-care, like taking a relaxing bath or spending time with friends, can make a significant difference in how you feel.

Connecting with other new moms can be incredibly helpful in managing postpartum emotions. Joining a support group or attending mommy and me classes can provide a sense of community and reassurance that you're not alone in your experiences. Sharing your thoughts and feelings with others who are going through similar challenges can be comforting and validating.

If you find that your postpartum emotions are persistently interfering with your daily life or if you're experiencing symptoms of depression or anxiety, it's essential to seek professional help. Postpartum depression and anxiety are common and treatable conditions. A healthcare provider can provide guidance, support, and, if necessary, recommend therapy or medication to help you navigate this challenging period.

Remember, managing postpartum emotions and mental health is an ongoing process. Be patient with yourself and allow yourself the time and space to heal and adjust. With proper self-care, support, and professional help if needed, you can navigate through this transformative period and enjoy the beautiful journey of motherhood.

Nurturing Your Relationship with Your Partner

As a new mom, your attention is understandably focused on your precious little one. However, it's important not to overlook the essential relationship you have with your partner. Maintaining a strong and healthy bond will not only benefit your own well-being but also provide a stable and loving environment for your baby. Here are some valuable tips for nurturing your relationship with your partner amidst the beautiful chaos of parenthood.

1. Communicate openly: Parenthood brings new challenges and responsibilities, so it's crucial to communicate openly with your partner. Talk about your feelings, concerns, and expectations, and listen attentively to their perspective. Regularly check in with each other to ensure that you are both on the same page and working together as a team.

2. Prioritize quality time: It's easy to get caught up in the never-ending cycle of feeding, changing diapers, and sleepless nights. However, setting aside quality time for just you and your partner is vital. Whether it's a weekly date night, a simple walk in the park, or even a cozy evening at home, make an effort to reconnect and enjoy each other's company.

3. Share parenting responsibilities: Parenting responsibilities can be overwhelming, so make sure to share the load with your partner. Divide tasks such as feeding, bathing, and putting the baby to sleep. This will not only reduce the workload but also allow both of you to bond with your little one individually.

4. Show appreciation: It's easy to take each other for granted during the demanding early months of parenthood. Take a moment each day

to express gratitude for your partner's efforts. A simple "thank you" or a small gesture can go a long way in making your partner feel valued and loved.

5. Keep the romance alive: While your focus may be on your baby, it's essential to keep the romance alive in your relationship. Surprise your partner with small gestures of affection, plan intimate moments together, and don't forget to say "I love you" regularly. Remember, a strong emotional connection is the foundation of a healthy relationship.

6. Seek support: Don't hesitate to ask for help when you need it. Reach out to family, friends, or support groups specifically designed for new parents. Taking care of your own well-being is crucial for maintaining a healthy relationship with your partner.

Remember, nurturing your relationship with your partner is an ongoing process. By prioritizing open communication, quality time, and appreciation, you can build a solid foundation that will support your family's journey into parenthood.

Seeking Support from Other New Moms and Communities

As a new mom, the journey of motherhood can often feel overwhelming and isolating. The good news is that you are not alone in this experience. Seeking support from other new moms and communities can be a game-changer, providing you with invaluable resources, advice, and a sense of belonging. In this subchapter, we will explore the importance of seeking support and the various ways you can connect with other new moms and communities.

One of the first things to understand is that seeking support is not a sign of weakness; it is a strength. By reaching out to others who are going through similar experiences, you create a network of understanding and empathy. This network can help you navigate the challenges, celebrate the victories, and share the joys of motherhood. Whether it's seeking advice on breastfeeding, sleep training, or simply finding a listening ear, there are countless benefits to connecting with other new moms.

One of the most accessible ways to find support is through online communities and forums. Joining groups specifically designed for new moms can be a great way to connect with others who are going through similar experiences. These communities often provide a safe space to ask questions, seek advice, and share your own insights. From Facebook groups to dedicated online forums, there are plenty of platforms where you can find support and build connections.

Another way to seek support is through local mom groups and meetups. These gatherings often provide an opportunity to meet other new moms in your area and form real-life friendships. Whether it's a breastfeeding support group, a postpartum exercise class, or a playgroup for babies, these communities offer a chance to connect with others who are on a similar journey.

Additionally, consider reaching out to friends and family who have recently become parents themselves. Their firsthand experience can be a valuable resource, offering practical advice and emotional support. Having a close circle of friends who understand the challenges and joys of motherhood can make a significant difference in your own well-being.

Remember, seeking support is not a one-way street. Be open to offering your support and sharing your own experiences with others. By building a community of support, you not only benefit yourself but also become a lifeline for other new moms who may be seeking guidance.

In conclusion, seeking support from other new moms and communities is an essential part of your journey as a first-time mom. By connecting with others, whether online or in person, you gain access to a wealth of knowledge, empathy, and friendship. Embrace the power of community and let it guide you through the ups and downs of motherhood.

Chapter 10: Celebrating Milestones: First Words, Steps, and Beyond

Encouraging Language Development and Communication Skills

One of the most incredible milestones in your baby's early years is their language development and communication skills. As a new mom, it's essential to foster and encourage this growth, as it lays the foundation for their future success in school and social interactions. In this subchapter, we will explore various strategies and activities to help you support your baby's language development journey.

1. Engage in Conversations: From the moment your baby is born, they're absorbing information from their surroundings. Talk to your baby using simple and repetitive language, making eye contact to capture their attention. Engaging in conversations helps develop their listening skills and understanding of speech patterns.

2. Read, Read, Read: Introduce books to your baby as early as possible. Choose colorful and interactive books with textures or sounds to capture their interest. Reading aloud to your baby not only exposes them to new words and concepts but also strengthens the bond between you.

3. Sing and Rhyme: Babies love the rhythm and melody of songs and nursery rhymes. Singing and reciting rhymes expose your baby to the natural flow and cadence of language. It also helps develop their memory and cognitive skills.

4. Play with Sounds: Encourage your baby to make different sounds by imitating their babbling and responding to their vocalizations. Use

toys that produce sounds, such as rattles or musical instruments, to engage their auditory senses.

5. Use Sign Language: Baby sign language can be an effective tool in enhancing communication skills. Teaching simple signs like "milk," "eat," or "more" can help your baby express their needs before they can speak.

6. Limit Screen Time: Excessive screen time can hinder language development. Ensure that your baby has limited exposure to screens and prioritize real-life interactions instead.

7. Encourage Social Interactions: Arrange playdates or join parent baby groups where your little one can interact with peers. Socialization plays a crucial role in language development as babies learn by observing and imitating others.

Remember, every baby develops at their own pace, so be patient and provide a nurturing environment that supports their individual journey. Celebrate each milestone, whether it's their first word or their ability to express themselves through gestures. By implementing these strategies, you are setting the stage for your baby's language development and communication skills, ensuring a happy and successful future.

Supporting Physical Development and Motor Skills

As a new mom, it's natural to be concerned about your baby's physical development and motor skills. Watching your little one grow and achieve new milestones is an exciting and rewarding experience. In this subchapter, we will explore various ways you can support your baby's physical development and help them reach their motor skill milestones with confidence.

One of the most crucial aspects of supporting physical development is providing a safe and stimulating environment for your baby. Ensure that your home is baby-proofed and free from potential hazards. Allow your baby plenty of space to move and explore, both indoors and outdoors, while keeping a watchful eye on their activities.

Tummy time is an essential activity that helps strengthen your baby's neck, shoulder, and back muscles. Encourage your baby to spend short periods of time on their tummy every day. This position will not only aid in developing their motor skills but also prevent flat spots on the back of their head.

Playing with your baby is an excellent way to support their physical development. Engage in activities that encourage reaching, grasping, and rolling over. Provide them with age-appropriate toys that stimulate their senses and encourage exploration. As they grow, introduce toys that promote crawling, standing, and walking.

Babywearing is another fantastic way to support your baby's physical development. Using a baby carrier or sling allows you to keep your baby close while leaving your hands free. This closeness promotes bonding and provides your baby with the opportunity to observe and learn from their surroundings.

Regular exercise is crucial for your baby's physical development. Encourage them to move their limbs by gently stretching and flexing their arms and legs. As they grow older, introduce activities like swimming, dancing, or even baby yoga to further enhance their motor skills.

Remember that each baby develops at their own pace, so it's essential to be patient and supportive. If you have concerns about your baby's physical development or motor skills, don't hesitate to consult with your pediatrician. They can provide expert advice and guidance tailored to your baby's individual needs.

By creating a safe and stimulating environment, engaging in playtime activities, and promoting regular exercise, you can support your baby's physical development and motor skills. Embrace this exciting journey and celebrate each milestone your little one achieves along the way.

Celebrating Your Baby's Firsts: Crawling, Walking, and Talking

Subchapter: Celebrating Your Baby's Firsts: Crawling, Walking, and Talking

Introduction:

As a new mom, every milestone your baby achieves is a reason for celebration. From their first adorable smile to their first steps, these precious moments mark the growth and development of your little one. In this subchapter, we will explore the exciting journey of your baby's firsts, focusing specifically on crawling, walking, and talking. Understanding and appreciating these milestones will not only help you track your baby's progress but also give you a sense of joy and accomplishment as a first-time mom.

Crawling:

One of the most anticipated firsts for every parent is when their baby starts to crawl. This milestone typically occurs between 6 to 10 months of age. We will discuss the various crawling styles, from the classic "army crawl" to the more advanced "hands-and-knees crawl." Alongside, we will provide tips on creating a safe and stimulating environment for your baby to explore. Celebrating your baby's crawling milestone can be as simple as capturing adorable photos or encouraging their newfound mobility through interactive play.

Walking:

The first wobbly steps your baby takes will undoubtedly bring tears of joy to your eyes. Typically, babies begin walking independently between 9 to 15 months of age. We will delve into the different stages of walking, from cruising along furniture to those exciting first unassisted steps. Offering guidance on supporting your baby's balance and coordination, we will also discuss the selection of appropriate footwear. Additionally, we will provide suggestions on how to celebrate this milestone, such as creating a dedicated walking zone in your home and organizing a small gathering to share the joy with loved ones.

Talking:
Your baby's first words are like music to your ears, marking the beginning of their language development. Around 12 months, you little one may utter their first recognizable word, gradually progressing to more complex sentences. We will explore the stages of language acquisition and offer fun activities to encourage speech development. Celebrating your baby's language milestones can involve engaging in conversations, reading together, and even creating a memory book with their early words and phrases.

Conclusion:
Celebrating your baby's firsts is an integral part of the joyous journey of motherhood. By understanding the significance of crawling, walking, and talking milestones, you can cultivate an environment that supports your baby's growth and development. As a new mom, relish in the excitement of these milestones, document their journey through photos and memories, and most importantly, cherish the precious moments of your baby's early achievements.

Embracing the Joys and Challenges of Parenthood

Becoming a parent is a life-altering experience filled with both incredible joys and unexpected challenges. For new moms, this journey is particularly unique as they navigate the uncharted waters of motherhood. In this subchapter, we will explore the many emotions, rewards, and trials that come with embracing the joys and challenges of parenthood.

The Joy of Parenthood: There is no greater joy than holding your newborn baby for the first time and feeling an overwhelming sense of love and protectiveness. As a new mom, your heart will swell with pride as you witness your child's first smile, hear their infectious laughter, and witness their milestones. Embracing these precious moments and cherishing the bond you share with your little one is a true blessing that will fill your life with immeasurable joy.

The Challenges of Parenthood: Parenthood also presents a myriad of challenges that can sometimes feel overwhelming. Adjusting to sleepless nights, managing the demands of breastfeeding or bottle feeding, and dealing with endless diaper changes can push new moms to their limits. It is essential to remember that it is okay to feel overwhelmed or inadequate at times. Parenthood is a learning process, and it takes time to adjust and find your rhythm. By seeking support from loved ones, joining parenting groups, and practicing self-care, you can overcome these challenges with resilience and grace.

Finding Balance: One of the most significant challenges new moms face is finding balance in their new role as a parent. It is essential to prioritize self-care and carve out time for your own well-being. Remember, a happy and fulfilled mom is better equipped to care for her baby. Explore different strategies such as setting realistic expectations, delegating tasks, and seeking support from your partner or loved ones to find a healthy balance between your needs and those of your child.

Building a Support System: Another crucial aspect of embracing parenthood is building a strong support system. Surrounding yourself with fellow new moms, experienced parents, or even joining online communities can provide a sense of belonging and a space to share your joys, concerns, and questions. Remember, you are not alone on this journey. By connecting with others who have gone through similar experiences, you can gain valuable insights and support.

In conclusion, embracing the joys and challenges of parenthood is a transformative experience that every new mom embarks upon. By cherishing the moments of joy, acknowledging the challenges, finding balance, and building a support system, you can navigate this beautiful journey with confidence and grace. Remember, you are capable, resilient, and deserving of all the happiness that comes with being a first-time mom.

Conclusion: A Journey of Love and Learning: Embracing the Adventure of Motherhood

Congratulations, new moms! You have embarked on a remarkable journey of love and learning – the adventure of motherhood. Throughout this book, we have provided you with a comprehensive guide to equip you with everything you need to know for a happy baby. Now, as we conclude this chapter, let us reflect on the incredible journey that lies ahead.

Motherhood is a unique and awe-inspiring experience, filled with joy, challenges, and countless moments of growth. It is a journey that no one can truly prepare you for, yet it is also one that will undoubtedly change your life in the most beautiful ways. As you navigate through the ups and downs, remember that you are not alone. There is a whole community of new moms who have walked this path before you and are here to support and uplift you.

Embracing the adventure of motherhood means embracing the unknown. It means surrendering to the unpredictable nature of raising a child and allowing yourself to be fully present in each moment. It means cherishing the little victories and finding strength in the face of adversity. Remember, it's okay to make mistakes – we all do. What truly matters is the love and dedication you bring to the journey.

As a new mom, it is crucial to prioritize self-care. Remember that taking care of yourself is just as important as taking care of your little one. Nurture your body, mind, and soul, as they are the foundation upon which you can build a happy and healthy family. Surround yourself with a support network of loved ones who can offer guidance, encouragement, and a helping hand when you need it most.

Throughout this book, we have covered a wide range of topics – from pregnancy and childbirth to feeding, sleep routines, and beyond. These are valuable tools that will assist you along the way, but it's essential to remember that every child is unique. Trust your instincts and embrace the learning process. Your baby will guide you, and together, you will forge an unbreakable bond.

In conclusion, dear new moms, this is just the beginning of an extraordinary adventure. Embrace the unknown, cherish the precious moments, and surround yourself with love and support. Motherhood is a constant learning experience, and as you navigate through each phase, remember to trust yourself and enjoy the journey. You are capable, strong, and filled with an abundance of love. May this book serve as a guiding light as you embark on this incredible adventure of motherhood.

Milton Keynes UK
Ingram Content Group UK Ltd.
UKHW020236221123
432980UK00016B/1225